GIRL. BOY. SEA.